Whose legs?

To Parents

Very young children develop their use of language through talking and listening to others talk. Sharing books together right from a very early age and talking about stories and pictures is one of the best ways to help develop and widen your child's experience and use of language.

This book is one of four play books, designed for children from the age of 2 years upwards. Each book contains a similar guessing or surprise element through the use of the split pages. Young children love this type of activity and will soon learn to follow or 'read' the book themselves, using the pictures.

The use of strong rhythm and repetition throughout each story also gives the child a pattern to remember the words by, so you may find after a number of readings your child knows the story off by heart. He or she may then want to join in or 'read' the book to you – children should be encouraged to do this because although they may not be decoding every word, they will be learning how to behave as readers and gaining in confidence.

Learning how books work is a crucial step and this early involvement with books will also help your child to see reading as a purposeful and enjoyable activity, right from the start. Like all the books in **The Parent and Child Programme**, these stories are intended for parents and children to share together. Here are some ways you may like to use this book with your child:

1. Reading to your child: always allow plenty of time for the child to look and talk about the pictures. As your child becomes familiar with the story, point to the words as you read, so the child sees that the print runs from left to right. Don't alert your child to the speech marks; children learn to ignore these if they are not pointed out and it will be some time before your child is ready to understand their use.

2. On further readings, pause and see if your child can say whether the animal has the right legs before you turn the page. Let your child join in with the reading as much or as little as he or she wants and never rush.

3. After a few readings see if your child remembers or guesses how each animal moves before turning the page.

4. Try to expand the theme of the book by relating it to your child's experiences – looking at pets or animals in the country or on television.

5. Above all, ensure that you both have fun with the book!

THE·PARENT·AND·CHILD·PROGRAMME

Whose legs?

Devised and written by
David Bennett

Illustrated by
Julie Lacome

The two funny legs that
you can see, are not
for you and not for me.

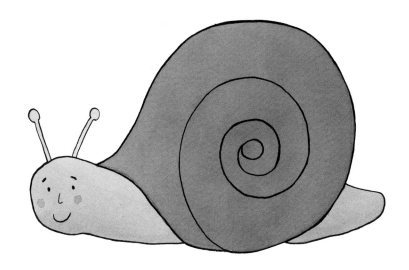

Whose legs can they be?

Do you know whose legs these are?

"Oh yes," says duck,
"as you can see,
these two thin legs
are right for me."

SNAKES

Written by Barrie Wade
Photographed by Tony Phelps
Illustrated by Andrew Midgley

Collins Educational
An Imprint of HarperCollinsPublishers

Contents

Introduction

This book is about the different types of snakes that live in Britain. It looks at the way they live, what they eat and how they reproduce. British snakes are becoming rare, so they should not be harmed or destroyed.

A smooth snake

A grass snake

An adder

Basking

Snakes are cold-blooded **reptiles**. They need to **bask** in the sunshine to warm their bodies before they can become active. They stretch themselves out to get as much sun as possible.

A smooth snake basking in the sun.

Movement

Snakes can move very quickly. They push themselves along by rippling the muscles underneath their bodies. Their scales grip the ground so that they don't slide backwards.

A smooth snake moving over a pile of sticks.

The whole body of the snake follows the movement of the head with a winding, wriggling motion.

Skin

Snakes' skins are leathery and scaly. When a snake grows, it has to shed its old skin and grow a new one. This may happen twice a year.

A smooth snake shedding its skin.

Part of a grass snake's skin. The eye sockets and the scales can be seen.

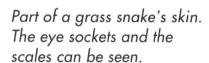

Tongue

A snake uses its forked tongue to taste and smell the air. It can sense with its tongue if food is nearby or if there is any danger.

A grass snake tasting the air.

Snakes in Britain

There are three different kinds of snakes in Britain: grass snakes, smooth snakes and adders. Dry areas, where there are small trees, shrubs and grasses, provide the ideal **habitat** for snakes.

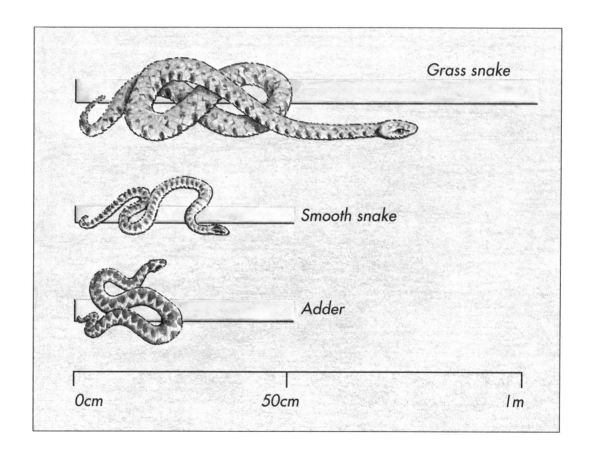

Grass snake

Smooth snake

Adder

0cm   50cm   1m

A comparison of the sizes of the three snakes. (Diagram not to scale)

Grass snakes

Grass snakes are completely harmless to humans. They are brownish green with black markings and have a yellow collar behind the head.

A large grass snake.

Grass snakes live on land, but they are excellent swimmers and can hunt in water. They eat frogs and toads, newts and tadpoles. Grass snakes can grow to more than one metre in length.

A grass snake in water.

Female grass snakes lay leathery eggs.
A grass snake may lay up to 30 eggs in
one **clutch**.

*These eggs look crushed, but there are live young
snakes inside them.*

When a young grass snake hatches from its egg, it breaks free from the **yolk sac** and is ready to wriggle away. It has a greyish black skin with a white collar.

A newly hatched grass snake.

Smooth snakes

Smooth snakes live on sandy **heathland**. Because this kind of land is disappearing, these snakes can only be found in the south of England. The smooth snake is the rarest reptile in Britain.

A smooth snake basking.

Smooth snakes grow to about half the size of grass snakes and can be brown, brownish green or grey in colour. They eat young birds, small **mammals** and lizards, but they are harmless to humans.

A smooth snake heading for cover.

The smooth snake gives birth to live young, up to ten at one time. The young snake is coiled up inside a bag of skin and it may take five hours to break out of it.

A smooth snake giving birth.

The young snake is visible through the bag of skin.

Young smooth snakes may stay with their
mother for a day or two. Then they leave to
live on their own.

A young smooth snake with its mother.

Adders

The adder is a **venomous** snake, and is dangerous to humans. If it is in danger it will coil up ready to strike. Adders have a zig-zag pattern on their bodies.

A coiled adder.

Adders grow to about the same length as smooth snakes, but their bodies are thicker. Adders usually eat lizards and small rodents such as mice. Male and female adders look different from each other. Female adders are brownish, but the male is black and white.

A male and a female adder.

To win a female, two male adders perform a kind of wrestling match. This is called a rivalry display.

Adders in a rivalry display.

The winning adder mates with the female.
Mating may last for several hours.

A male and a female adder mating.

Like the smooth snake, the female adder gives birth to live young. She may have up to ten snakes at one time. All the young look like their mother at first. The young males will change colour when they grow older.

A female adder with her young.

Index

Glossary

bask to lie in the warmth of the sun

clutch a batch of eggs laid at any one time

habitat the natural home of a plant or animal

heathland a large open area of rough grass, with few trees and sandy soil

reptile a cold-blooded animal with a scaly skin. Usually, the females lay eggs.

mammal a warm blooded animal with a backbone. The female mammal does not lay eggs. She feeds her babies with milk from her own body.

venomous poisonous. The word comes from *venom* which is the poison that some snakes and insects inject into their prey by biting them.

yolk sac the part of an egg which provides food for the developing snake

23

Fascinating Facts

- Snakes can live for up to twenty-five years.
- Snakes never wink or blink because they don't have eyelids. Also, because they don't have ears, they have to feel sounds by picking up vibrations from the ground.
- The world's largest snake is the *reticulated python* from Asia which can be up to 10m long. This is longer than a double-decker bus.
- The world's heaviest snake is the *anaconda* which is found in South America. It can weigh up to 200kg, which is more than a baby elephant and is so heavy that it has to spend much of the time in the water.
- The world's smallest snake is the *thread snake* or *bootlace snake,* from the Caribbean. This snake is usually less than 15cm in length, smaller than your shoelace!